Politics, Minerals, and Survival

Proceedings of a Symposium Sponsored by the
Society of Economic Geologists and the
Mining and Exploration Division, Society
of Mining Engineers, American Institute
of Mining, Metallurgical and Petroleum Engineers
At Dallas, Texas, February 1974

Politics, Minerals, and Survival

Edited by

Ralph W. Marsden

Published for the
Society of Economic Geologists Foundation, Inc.
by
The University of Wisconsin Press

Published 1975
The University of Wisconsin Press
Box 1379, Madison, Wisconsin 53701

The University of Wisconsin Press, Ltd.
70 Great Russell Street, London

First printing

Printed in the United States of America

For LC CIP information see the colophon

ISBN 0-299-06810-2 cloth, 0-299-06814-5 paper

Contents

v

Figures

Tables

Preface

A symposium, "Politics, Minerals, and Survival," jointly sponsored by the Society of Economic Geologists and the Mining and Exploration Division, Society of Mining Engineers of the American Institute of Mining, Metallurgical and Petroleum Engineers, was held at Dallas, Texas, on February 28, 1974. This symposium was a sequel to another held on November 15, 1972, in Minneapolis, Minnesota, at the joint annual meeting of the Society of Economic Geologists and the Geological Society of America. The Minneapolis symposium, "The Mineral Position of the United States, 1975-2000," which has been published by the University of Wisconsin Press, focused attention on minerals in the domestic and world picture, with emphasis on the future but with particular reference to the next quarter-century. Since the United States is rapidly moving into new areas of concern with new problems of mineral supply, there is a need for understanding and analysis of current and future problems so that reasonable solutions can be found. It is hoped that bringing together experts to discuss topics within their special knowledge will develop a better understanding regarding the role of mineral commodities in our society and the solutions of problems affecting that role.

The Dallas symposium was organized by the Society of Economic Geologists' Committee for Information on Mineral Problems. The committee includes the following members: Donald A. Brobst, United States Geological Survey;

John J. Collins, American Smelting and Refining Company; Edward H. Eakland, Mineral Exploration Company; Ralph W. Marsden, University of Minnesota, Duluth (chairman); John B. Patton, Indiana Geological Survey; A. A. Socolow, Pennsylvania Geological Survey; and Robert J. Wright, American Metal Climax, Inc. When initial plans were made for the symposium in February 1973 at the Chicago meeting of the Society of Economic Geologists and AIME, we did not envision the dramatic impact that energy would suddenly have on world economics and public concerns. The term *energy crisis* is now a household phrase in the United States. Whether considered as a crisis or as a major inconvenience, the problems of the occurrence, production, distribution, and supply of petroleum and natural gas are now real to the average citizen.

This is both good news and bad. It is good that government, industry, and the public have received a warning that more severe problems may be ahead. This warning, if properly recognized, will permit the development of plans and programs that may solve or greatly diminish the impact of these problems. But there remains a common lack of understanding of the complexity and the extent of the interrelationships between energy and other mineral commodities and our everyday activities. The public is accustomed to abundant mineral products, readily available. In the past, much has been heard about problems of the oversupply of minerals, so that a scarcity of energy sources now seems sudden, improbable, and unnecessary. The chapter by E. N. Cameron in this volume, his presidential address to the Society of Economic Geologists at the February 1974 symposium, directs attention to vital aspects of the current mineral situation.

In their concerns for energy most people do not recognize that we may be approaching a time when a similar short fall of supply for other mineral products may develop. We tend to take for granted that minerals will be available when needed. The so-called "hard minerals," as contrasted to "energy materials," may also have problems regarding production, supply, and distribution. For some mineral commodities, the supply problems may be more severe in the long term than an adequate supply of energy.

At this time we find the public awakened to the need of environmental protection, pollution control, conservation of dwindling resources, and other factors that influence political, public, and societal attitudes toward the minerals industry. It is evident that a reasonable balance must be attained between the various societal needs so this industry can produce enough minerals to satisfy the basic requirements of the American economy. Solutions to many problems require political action. This action should be based on evaluations well grounded on facts.

With this rather fluid situation in mind, we selected five experts who will focus their attention on the present mineral situation, on politics, on financial aspects, on an industry viewpoint, and on the problems of the survival of our present life-style. These authors represent a variety of backgrounds and concerns. They come from government, the industrial-political sector, and the financial, industrial, and academic segments of the mineral resource community. Their thoughts and judgments are presented in this volume.

We wish to acknowledge the encouragement and aid given in the development of the symposium by E. F. Osborn and E. N. Cameron. Both are past presidents of the Society of Economic Geologists. We are grateful for the assistance of

Ernest K. Lehmann of the Mining and Exploration Division, Society of Mining Engineers, AIME, and S. C. Creasy of the Society of Economic Geologists in making arrangements for the meeting. We also acknowledge with our thanks the advice and counsel of Paul C. Henshaw and A. E. Weissenborn.

Ralph W. Marsden

Duluth, Minnesota
November 1974

Contributors

C. H. BURGESS

Vice President and Assistant to the President, Kennecott Copper Corporation, New York, New York

EUGENE N. CAMERON

Charles R. Van Hise Distinguished Professor of Geology, Department of Geology and Geophysics, University of Wisconsin—Madison

C. THOMAS HOUSEMAN

Vice President, Technical Director—Mining, The Chase Manhattan Bank, New York, New York

JOHN D. MORGAN, JR.

Assistant Director, Mineral Position Analysis, Bureau of Mines, Department of the Interior, Washington, D.C.

WILLIAM I. POWELL

Solicitor, American Mining Congress, Washington, D.C.

Politics, Minerals, and Survival

1

John D. Morgan, Jr.

The Mineral Position of the United States, 1974

Minerals are the lifeblood of any industrialized civilization. Annually, the economy of the United States requires over 4 billion tons of new mineral supplies (see fig. 1.1).

In 1974 the gross national product of the United States reached a new annual high of $1,397 billion. The value of energy and processed materials of mineral origin produced in the United States in 1974 was estimated to be more than $210 billion. This total came from mineral raw materials of domestic origin valued at $55 billion (see fig. 1.2), supplemented by imports of raw and processed mineral materials valued at $42 billion. Imports were, however, offset to some degree by exports of raw and processed minerals valued at $18 billion, leaving a net mineral-related deficit of the order of $24 billion. Crude and refined petroleum and iron and steel were the major items contributing to the net deficit position (see fig. 1.3). For production of major metals and minerals see table 1.1. Domestic production of most nonmetallics is shown in table 1.2. Demand for minerals was stimulated in part by business expenditures for new plant and equipment estimated at $112 billion, while the value of new construction put into place was $134 billion. Demand for motor vehicles also stimulated demand for minerals as about one-fifth of our

3

ABOUT 40,000 POUNDS OF NEW MINERAL MATERIALS ARE REQUIRED ANNUALLY FOR EACH U.S. CITIZEN

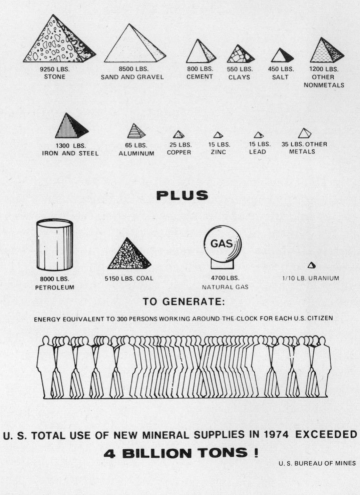

| 9250 LBS.
STONE | 8500 LBS.
SAND AND GRAVEL | 800 LBS.
CEMENT | 550 LBS.
CLAYS | 450 LBS.
SALT | 1200 LBS.
OTHER
NONMETALS |

| 1300 LBS.
IRON AND STEEL | 65 LBS.
ALUMINUM | 25 LBS.
COPPER | 15 LBS.
ZINC | 15 LBS.
LEAD | 35 LBS. OTHER
METALS |

PLUS

| 8000 LBS.
PETROLEUM | 5150 LBS. COAL | 4700 LBS.
NATURAL GAS | 1/10 LB. URANIUM |

TO GENERATE:

ENERGY EQUIVALENT TO 300 PERSONS WORKING AROUND-THE-CLOCK FOR EACH U.S. CITIZEN

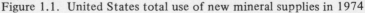

U. S. TOTAL USE OF NEW MINERAL SUPPLIES IN 1974 EXCEEDED
4 BILLION TONS !
U. S. BUREAU OF MINES

Figure 1.1. United States total use of new mineral supplies in 1974

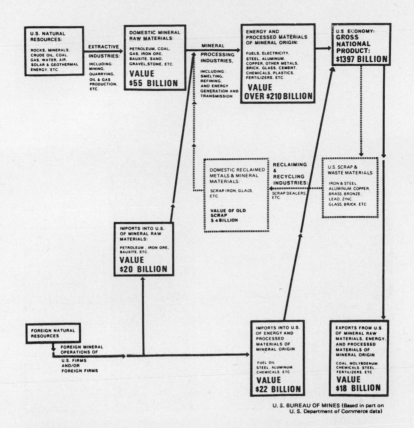

Figure 1.2. The role of minerals in the United States economy (estimated values for 1974)

steel and proportional quantities of many other minerals are used therein; 1974 production of new automobiles totaled 7,324,508 units, and truck production totaled 2,744,637 units.

The wholesale price indexes of major mineral commodity groups increased; the 1974 indexes based on 1967 = 100, were as follows: metals and metal products, 171.9; nonmetallic mineral products, 153.2; chemicals and allied

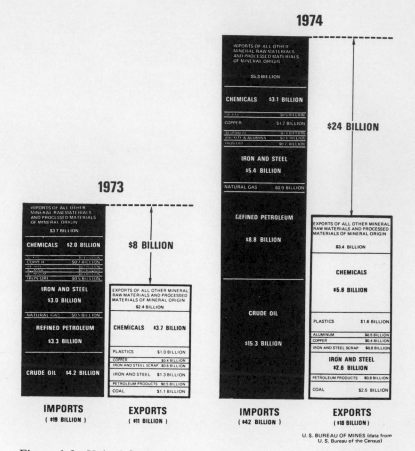

Figure 1.3. United States imports and exports of raw and processed minerals

products, 146.8; and fuels and related products and power, 208.3. Domestic price controls were alleged to have created a number of anomalies in the mineral industry in 1973, including such diverse impacts as creating domestic "shortages" of ammonium nitrate for fertilizers and explosives, of roof bolts for coal mine safety, and of domestic copper, lead, zinc, and other materials in instances where world prices rose significantly above domestic prices and where United States export controls were either not in effect or inadequate. In his Economic Report to the Congress of February 1, 1974, the president recognized the importance of free markets stating, "In the past several years, under the pressure of emergency conditions, we have made great, but temporary, departures from reliance on free prices and free markets. In special circumstances and for short periods these departures have been helpful. But taken together, these experiences have confirmed the view that the free market is, in general, our most efficient system of economic organization, and that sustained and comprehensive suppression of it will not solve the inflation problem." In line with this philosophy, price controls on all metals except steel, copper, and aluminum were lifted completely in December of 1973, and controlled rises in some of these product areas were permitted. All wage-price controls expired on April 30, 1974, except those on petroleum.

The "energy crisis" of late 1973 naturally led to questions as to whether the United States might not also be facing a potential "mineral crisis" in nonfuel mineral materials. Part of this concern stemmed from the significant energy inputs into minerals processing, because approximately one-fourth of all United States energy is used in winning and fabricating mineral materials, including steel, aluminum, cement, ceramics, chemicals, and plastics; consequently, significantly higher energy prices, and possible energy shortages, have a great impact on mineral processing. Concern also arises from the possibility of OPEC-like actions on the part of other raw-material-producing nations, although the diversity of suppliers, the needs for continuity of income to low-income producing nations, the postponability of some demands, and the possibilities

Table 1.1. Selected Data on United States Metal and Mineral Production

Item	Units	1972	1973	1974*
Value of Energy and Processed Minerals	billion U.S. dollars	160.	175.	210.
U.S. Domestic Raw Mineral Production	billion U.S. dollars	32.2	36.8	54.9
Fuels	billion U.S. dollars	22.3	25.2	41.6
Other Nonmetalics	billion U.S. dollars	6.5	7.4	8.2
Metals from U.S. ores	billion U.S. dollars	3.4	4.2	5.1
Bituminous Coal	million s. tons	595.	592.	590.
Steel (raw)	million s. tons	133.	151.	145.
Steel (mill products and castings)	million s. tons	93.4	113.3	106.9
Iron castings	million s. tons	16.4	18.1	17.0
Iron Ore (production)	million l. tons	75.4	87.7	83.0
Iron (purchased scrap)	million s. tons	47.1	50.9	54.0
Aluminium (primary)	s. tons	4,122,000	4,529,000	4,890,000
Aluminium (secondary)	s. tons	946,000	1,038,000	1,000,000
Bauxite	million l. tons	1.8	1.9	2.0
Copper (mine)	s. tons	1,665,000	1,718,000	1,588,000
Copper (refined—new)	s. tons	1,873,000	1,868,000	1,620,000
Copper (refined—secondary)	s. tons	423,000	465,000	500,000
Lead (mine)	s. tons	619,000	603,000	677,000
Lead (refined—primary plus antimonial)	s. tons	688,000	688,000	670,000
Lead (secondary)	s. tons	617,000	654,000	620,000

Zinc (mine)	s. tons	478,000	479,000	492,000
Zinc (primary plus redistilled)	s. tons	707,000	628,000	625,000
Magnesium (primary)	s. tons	121,000	122,000	withheld
Molybdenum	million lbs.	112.1	115.9	115.
Nickel (refined metal from U.S. ores)	s. tons	13,226	12,937	12,500
Nickel (secondary)	s. tons	35,926	33,295	34,000
Tungsten	s. tons	3,523	3,530	3,875
Vanadium (production–recoverable)	million lbs	9.8	8.8	withheld
Antimony (primary–smelter)	s. tons	13,344	17,206	14,500
Mercury (mine)	76-lb. flasks	7,333	2,171	1,700
Mercury (secondary)	76-lb. flasks	12,651	10,329	9,000
Gold (mine)	million tr. oz.	1.45	1.18	1.12
Gold (refinery–secondary)	million tr. oz.	2.10	1.80	1.80
Silver (mine)	million tr. oz.	37.2	37.8	33.8
Silver (refinery–secondary)	million tr. oz.	31.1	34.6	55.2
Platinum Group Metals (mine)	thousand tr. oz.	17.	20.	18.
Platinum Group Metals (refinery–secondary)	thousand tr. oz.	256.	266.	340.
Tin (mine)	l. tons	small	small	small
Tin (smelter)	l. tons	4,300	4,500	5,500
Tin (secondary)	l. tons	20,180	20,477	20,000
Uranium (U_3O_8 concentrates)	s. tons	13,667	13,588	12,600

*1974 data are preliminary.
Source: U.S. Bureau of Mines.

Table 1.2. 1974 United States Domestic Mine Production of Major Non-metallic Minerals, Change from 1973, and Significant Foreign Trade (all data in millions of short tons)

	Mine production	Change	Foreign trade
Asbestos	0.11	down 25%	Net imports 0.74
Barite	1.1	none	Net imports 0.72
Boron	1.2	down 2%	Net exports 0.24
Bromine	0.22	up 5%	Net exports 0.03
Cement (manufactured)	84.	down 2%	Net imports 5.2
Clays	61.	down 5%	Net exports 2.4
Diatomite	0.66	up 8%	Net exports 0.18
Feldspar	0.79	none	Net exports 0.02
Fluorspar	0.19	down 22%	Net imports 1.26
Gypsum	12.4	down 8%	Net imports 7.4
Ilmenite	0.76	down 6%	Net imports 0.35
Lime (manufactured)	21.9	up 4%	Net imports 0.4
Mica (scrap and flake)	0.13	down 25%	negligible
Peat	0.73	up 15%	Net imports 0.35
Perlite	0.75	none	not available
Phosphate Rock	44.7	up 6%	Net exports 12.8
Potash	2.55	down 2%	Net imports 3.53
Pumice	3.49	down 8%	Net imports 0.30
Salt	46.2	up 5%	Net imports 3.3
Sand and Gravel	904.	down 8%	Net exports 1.7
Sodium Carbonate (natural)	3.94	up 6%	Net exports 0.29
Sodium Carbonate (manufactured)	3.51	down 9%	
Sodium Sulphate (natural)	0.67	none	Net imports 0.30
Sodium Sulphate (manufactured)	0.67	down 12%	
Stone	981.	down 7%	negligible
Sulfur (Frasch)	8.90	up 5%	Net exports 0.45
Sulfur (recovered from refining)	2.86	up 6%	
Sulfur (other)	1.11	up 10%	
Talc, Soapstone, and Pyrophyllite	1.25	none	Net exports 0.16
Vermiculite	0.34	down 6%	not available

Source: U.S. Bureau of Mines

of substitutions are factors which would appear to make OPEC-like actions more difficult and less productive than was the case with respect to petroleum. These problems were recognized at the highest levels, however, and the president, in his January 1974 State of the Union Message, said: "It is also imperative that we review our current and prospective supplies of other basic commodities. I have therefore directed that a comprehensive report and policy analysis be made concerning this crucial matter so that government actions can properly anticipate and help avoid other damaging shortages." And in his February 1974 Budget Message he stated: "The adverse impact of energy shortages on the economy could be aggravated by shortages of other raw materials. A comprehensive study on supplies of metal ores and other basic resources and our needs for them is now underway. This study will help insure that our policies properly anticipate potential problems."

In mid-1973 the secretary of the interior issued his Second Report under the Mining and Minerals Policy Act of 1970. Stating that "development of domestic mineral resources is not keeping pace with domestic demand," he cited nine major problem areas confronting the mining, minerals, metal, mineral reclamation, and energy industries as follows:

(1) Mineral imports have an unfavorable impact upon the U.S. balance of trade and upon the U.S. balance of payments;
(2) Expropriations, confiscations, and forced modifications of agreements have severely modified the flow to the U.S. of some foreign mineral materials produced by U.S. firms operating abroad, and have made other materials more costly;
(3) U.S. industry is encountering greater competition from foreign nations and supranational groups in developing new foreign

mineral supplies and in assuring the long-term flow of minerals
to the United States;

(4) Development of the U.S. transportation net is not keeping pace
with demand, thus seriously affecting the energy and minerals
industries;

(5) Removal of billions of tons of minerals annually from the earth
contributes to a variety of disturbances;

(6) The U.S. mining, minerals, metal, and mineral reclamation industries are encountering increasing difficulty in financing
needed expansion of capacity and the introduction of new or
improved technology;

(7) Management of the resources of the public lands, including the
continental shelves, must be improved;

(8) The factual basis for the formulation and implementation of
environmental regulations must be improved, so that man and
nature are properly protected with minimum dislocation of
important economic activities; and

(9) The U.S. Government information base for the conduct of its
mineral responsibilities is grossly inadequate.

A number of corrective legislative recommendations
were made. These included creation of a Department of
Energy and Natural Resources, provision of an organic act
for the Bureau of Land Management, revision of the mineral leasing laws, regulation of surface mining activities,
amendment of the Natural Gas Act, construction of deep-
water ports, and modification of right-of-way limitations.
Only the latter, as the Alaska Pipeline Bill, was enacted
into law, the other recommendations being carried forward
into the considerations of the Congress in 1974. Also in
mid-1973 the National Commission on Materials Policy
issued its "Final Report," which made 177 detailed recommendations, those affecting minerals being in close agreement with the Mineral Policy Report. Perhaps the most

significant recommendation of the NCMP was that "it should be the policy of the United States to rely on market forces as a prime determinant of the mix of imports and domestic production in the field of materials but at the same time decrease and prevent wherever necessary a dangerous or costly dependence on imports."

While the economy of the United States has grown over the years, that of the world has increased even more, so that today the country is finding ever increasing competition when it comes to acquiring needed raw materials. At the same time, the United States is also finding it increasingly difficult to sell many manufactured articles in world markets to pay for imported raw materials. Two decades ago the United States produced about one-half of the world's steel (see fig. 1.4), whereas today, despite growth, it now produces only one-fifth. Similarly, where it once produced larger fractions, today it produces only one-fourth of the world's refined petroleum and one-third of the world's aluminum metal (see fig. 1.5). And the country is dependent upon imports for substantial portions of a number of important mineral materials (see fig. 1.6). The relative roles of domestic mining, secondary recovery, and imports over the past two decades are shown graphically for major commodities in Figure 1.7, for iron and steel; Figure 1.8, nonferrous metals; Figure 1.9, fertilizers; Figure 1.10, major nonmetallic construction materials; and Figure 1.11, energy sources.

The natural resources of the United States are vast, but to be useful to man, natural resources must be found, developed, and processed. The natural resources of any nation are related to its size, its geology, and its location on the earth. Only one nation, the Union of Soviet Socialist Republics, substantially exceeds the United States in

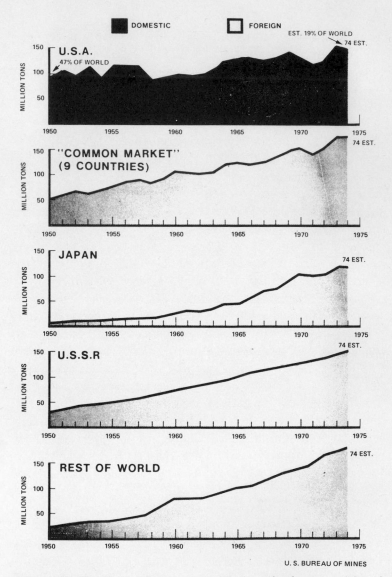

Figure 1.4. The United States now produces only about one-fifth of the world's steel

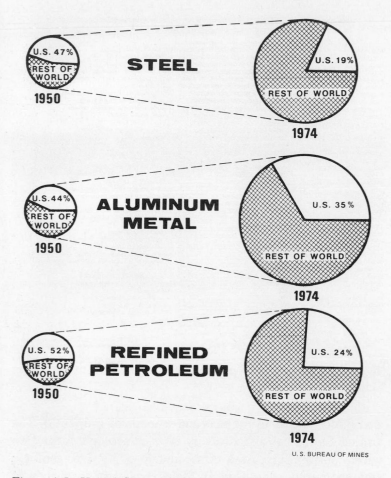

Figure 1.5. United States production in relation to the rest of the world: steel, aluminum, and refined petroleum

land area, and only four other nations, the People's Republic of China, Canada, Brazil, and Australia, have land areas about the size of the United States. In addition to its land area, the United States has extensive continental shelves

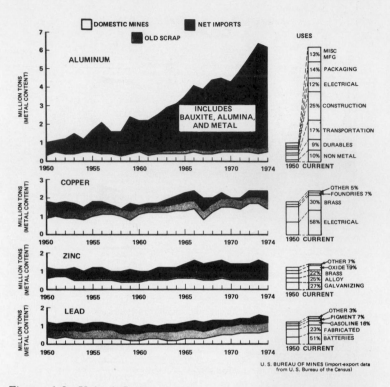

Figure 1.8. United States supplies and uses of major nonferrous metals

than forests and other agricultural resources, because most mineral deposits are located out of sight below the earth's surface. Our deepest mines have penetrated somewhat beyond a mile only in a few places and our deepest wells to about six miles in a few places. Our deepest dredges now operate in only a few hundred feet of water; yet it is nearly four thousand miles to the center of the earth. Through the study of geological maps and the making of

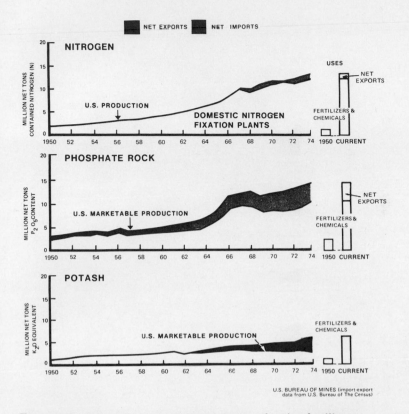

Figure 1.9. United States supplies and uses of major fertilizers

complex geophysical and geochemical measurements skilled geologists can, in some cases, infer what lies below the surface. Obviously, in areas where the rock strata are relatively uniform and cover many square miles, inferences as to what may be found below are better than in areas of very complex geology where heat, pressure, and earth movements have greatly deformed the rocks.

Mineral deposits that have been found, adequately

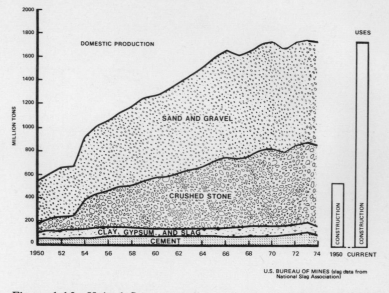

U.S. BUREAU OF MINES (slag data from National Slag Association)

Figure 1.10. United States supplies and uses of major nonmetallic construction materials

drilled to determine their content of valuable minerals, and that can be mined, processed, and converted into useful materials with known technology at reasonable prices, are commonly called "reserves." (For example, the rocks of the earth's crust average 5 percent iron; the United States has vast resources of rocks containing more than 5 percent iron; the iron ore reserves of the United States are 10,000,000,000 tons, which in turn contain 2,000,000,000 tons of recoverable iron metal; compare this to United States steel production of 145,000,000 tons in 1974).

Agricultural materials are generally renewable in relatively short time spans; some crops can be raised four or five times a year, annual cycles are common, and softwood trees can be raised on fifteen- to twenty-year cycles. Min-

U.S. DEMAND FOR
MAJOR ENERGY SOURCES

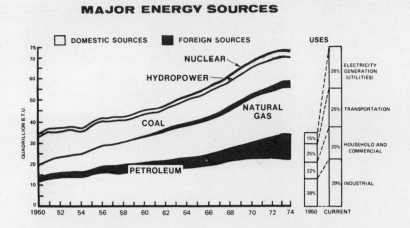

CONSUMPTION OF ENERGY BY SOURCES
(1974)

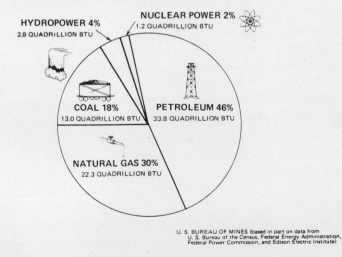

U. S. BUREAU OF MINES (based in part on data from
U. S. Bureau of the Census, Federal Energy Administration,
Federal Power Commission, and Edison Electric Institute)

Figure 1.11. United States demand for major energy sources and
consumption of energy by sources (1974)

eral deposits, however, normally are formed only over much longer periods of time, usually tens of millions or hundreds of millions of years. Consequently, the total supply of all minerals accessible to man in the earth's crust is, to all practical purposes, relatively fixed, and hence mineral materials are generally of greater concern to nations with heavy industry.

Other than in nuclear processes, elements are neither created nor destroyed; man's processing merely combines them in certain ways, recombines them, or reduces combinations into elemental form. Thus, the materials industries are engaged in extracting elements from natural materials, and/or combining or recombining them into forms more useful to man. Nature itself is constantly engaged in vast processing activities, in which the "carbon-oxygen," "nitrogen," and "hydrologic" cycles are major examples.

For most purposes there are great interchangeabilities in materials. Rubber, for example, can be made from natural latex from rubber trees, carbon and hydrogen from alcohol from grain or other agricultural materials, carbon and hydrogen from hydrocarbons from petroleum, natural gas, coal, etc.; and buildings can be constructed from steel, aluminum, copper, glass, stone, slate, concrete, tile, wood, plastics, plywood and many, many other materials.

In specialized technological applications in which a multiplicity of properties are required (for example, a combination of strength, electrical conductivity, temperature resistance, corrosion resistance, and creep resistance), the available materials are much more limited. If we are to achieve substantial breakthroughs in energy, we must have greatly improved temperature-resistant materials, yet Figure 1.12 shows that there are only a very limited number of elements which possess such properties.

Today improvement of domestic productivity in the mining, minerals, metal, mineral reclamation, and energy industries requires accelerated development of new and improved technology and rapid introduction thereof into all stages including: exploration, mining and petroleum and natural gas production, processing, use, and recovery and recycling. In all of these stages appropriate provision must be made for the health and safety of workers and for environmental enhancement through minimizing air, water, and land pollution, and encouraging land restoration and esthetic improvement.

Further, because many important minerals are initially large bulk items, mineral production is heavily dependent on the United States transportation infrastructure (see fig. 1.13). Consequently, improvements in rail and water transportation are of direct interest to major segments of the domestic mineral industry.

The resources of industry, government, and academia must be brought to bear on current major problems, including:

1. discovery and assessment of resources presently untouched by our deepest mines and wells;

2. development of safe and efficient coal mining systems to significantly increase underground extraction ratios from the present level of about one-half;

3. development of improved petroleum recovery methods to significantly increase extraction ratios above the present level of about one-third;

4. development of underground surface mining methods to minimize degradation of the land surface, subsidence, and harm to surface and subsurface waters;

5. development of clean-burning solid, liquid, and gas-

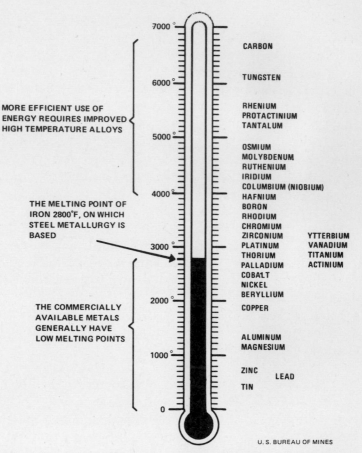

Figure 1.12. Degrees fahrenheit melting point for all known elements above iron and major metals melting at lower temperatures

eous fuels from coal, petroleum, and other energy materials;

6. improvement of combustion processes to increase efficiency and to reduce emissions of fumes and particulates;

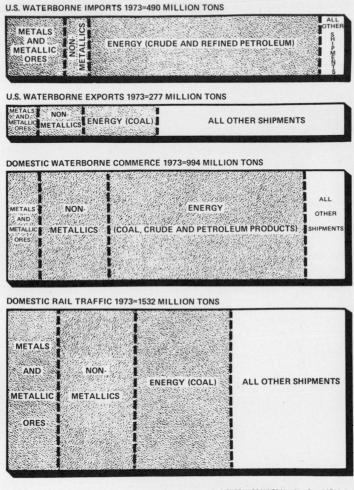

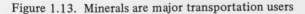

U. S. BUREAU OF MINES (data from Corps of Engineers
and Interstate Commerce Commission)

Figure 1.13. Minerals are major transportation users

7. improvement of electricity generation, transmission, and conversion methods;

8. development of new energy sources, including geo-thermal and solar;

9. development of stronger, lighter, corrosion-resistant, and temperature-resistant materials;

10. improvement of recycling techniques to conserve natural materials and energy and to promote environmental enhancement; and

11. stimulation of measures to conserve energy and materials in actual or potential short supply.

In the Department of the Interior, the Geological Survey and the Bureau of Mines (under the immediate direction of the assistant secretary, energy and minerals, and the secretary) are working closely together in the furtherance of the above objectives to improve the domestic minerals position of the United States.

2

William I. Powell

Politics:
A Whole New Ball Game
for the Mining Industry,
Both Domestic and Foreign

Each Congress has before it some 15,000 proposals ranging in length from one or two pages to literally hundreds of pages. A large proportion of these measures, if enacted, would directly affect the minerals industry. Before consideration is given to a proposal by the Congress, it must be formally introduced by one or more members of either legislative body. Proposed legislation must be brought to the attention of someone in Congress. There are various sources for legislative ideas.

1. Legislation often is conceived by a member of Congress based on statements made during his election campaign.

2. Many proposals may emanate either from constituents acting individually or collectively in trade associations, such as the American Mining Congress, labor unions, or other organized associations, in pursuit of their constitutional right to petition Congress for new laws or for needed amendments in existing laws. Excellent laws commonly result from trade association suggestions since such groups have considerable knowledge and expertise on mat-

27

ters affecting the membership of the organization and how best it can serve the public interest.

3. A much used method to get new legislative ideas before Congress is known as an "executive communication" from the president, a cabinet member, or the head of an independent governmental agency. Such proposals are usually introduced by the chairman or a leading member of the committee concerned.

Bills may originate in either the House of Representatives or in the Senate. The one exception, required by the Constitution, is that all bills for raising revenue must originate in the House of Representatives. Speaking only of procedures in the House, after a bill has been introduced it is assigned a number and then referred to the appropriate committee by the leadership with the aid of the parliamentarian.

Committee consideration is probably the most important phase of the congressional process. Each committee is provided with a professional and clerical staff to assist the members in the innumerable administrative details and other matters involved in the consideration of bills. In committee, the most intensive consideration is given to a proposed measure, and here interested persons are afforded their opportunity to be heard. The initial consideration is often done in subcommittees prior to final committee action.

Normally, one of the first actions taken by a committee is to refer the bill to the departments or agencies of the executive department concerned with the subject matter, for their comments and recommendations. Prior to a department or agency filing its report on a bill, the report is submitted to the Office of Management and Budget to determine whether or not the proposal is consistent with the program of the president.

Public hearings are held which last from one day to several months, depending on the length and subject matter of the bill. These are followed by what is known as "the marking-up session," which is a review of the proposed legislation. This session is now commonly open to the public as a result of recent changes in the procedures of the Congress. Following this, the committee considers the bill in executive session (closed to the public) and votes to report the bill favorably, or to table it, the latter action normally being effective in preventing further action on the bill.

If the bill receives favorable action by the committee, a report is written to accompany the proposal which, if the bill becomes law, is probably the most valuable single element of the legislative history of a new law. Such reports are used by the courts, executive department and agencies, and the public generally as a meaningful source of information regarding the purpose and meaning of the new law.

There are many ways that bills approved by a committee can be taken up for consideration on the floor of the House. Measures considered to be more important and urgent than others can be taken up out of numerical order by obtaining approval of the "Rules" Committee. The Rules Committee thus provides a degree of selectivity in the order that legislation is considered in the House. Once a "rule" has been granted, the bill is placed on the House Calendar either under a "closed rule" (no amendments permitted), with a limitation on time for debate, or an "open rule" (amendments permitted), also with a limitation on time for debate.

Following consideration by the House, the bill is either defeated or passed and sent to the Senate, where somewhat similar procedures are followed. The Senate, after its normal consideration of a House-passed bill, either adopts the bill, possibly with Senate amendments, or rejects it. If the Senate amends and then adopts the bill, the next step is for each body to appoint conferees to meet and work out their differences. When this is accomplished and the House and Senate adopt the report of the Conference Committee, this legislation as approved by both bodies is sent to the president for his approval or veto.

The foregoing is a much simplified procedure of how a new law or changes in an existing law come about.

I think it worthwhile to touch on some of the important proposals which have recently become law, or those now under active consideration by Congress which directly affect the minerals industry. As you will see, some bills which have been enacted and pending proposals, if enacted, will certainly create a "new ball game" for domestic and foreign mining operations.

First, I would like to list just a few such legislative proposals and then comment briefly on where some of them stand, the possibility of enactment into law, and so on.

1. (a) S. 425: the "surface mining" bill, which passed the Senate by a large majority on October 9, 1973.
   (b) H.R. 11500: the surface mining counterpart in the House now under actual consideration.
2. (a) S. 268: the Land Use Planning Act of 1973, which has passed the Senate.
   (b) H.R. 10294: the Land Use Planning Act counterpart in the House. The House Rules Committee is holding up House floor consideration of this bill.

3. (a) S. 2589: the National Energy Emergency Act (vetoed by President Nixon).

(b) H.R. 11450: the National Energy Emergency Act counterpart in the House. (A "briefed down" version of these bills is now under consideration in Congress.)

4. (a) S. 1283: the National Energy Research and Development Act of 1973, which passed the Senate on December 7, 1973.

(b) H.R. 11510: the House counterpart of the National Energy Research and Development Act, which passed the House on December 19, 1973.

5. (a) H.R. 12014: a bill that would establish a public corporation to explore and develop all *oil shale* energy resources on federal lands.

(b) S. 2506: the Senate counterpart on the establishment of a public corporation for the development of minerals in the public domain.

6. Tax policy and trade policy: a large number of bills have been introduced which would change the tax treatment of foreign oil and gas operations and which could well apply to other mineral operations at some future date. The bills would eliminate depletion on foreign petroleum production and also adversely affect the foreign tax credit.

7. (a) S. 1040: a bill which would amend the mineral leasing laws to include all minerals.

(b) H.R. 5442: the counterpart bill in the House with respect to the mineral leasing laws.

8. (a) S. 2744: a bill that would establish an Energy Research and Development Administration and a new Nuclear Energy Commission.

(b) H.R. 11510: the counterpart bill in the House on ERDA and NEC.

9. (a) S. 2776: a bill that would reorganize and consoli-

date federal government energy operations into a new
Federal Energy Administration.
(b) H. R. 11793: the FEA counterpart bill in the
House.

The foregoing bills are a few of the proposals pending
before Congress which directly affect the minerals industry, some adversely, some which could prove helpful to
our industry and the public in general. In order to drive
home the proposition that the minerals industry is faced
with a whole new ball game both here and abroad, with
vast new rulings and standards of operation flowing from
recent legislative enactments as well as from proposals now
pending before Congress, I would like to go into greater
detail with respect to a few of these proposals that affect
not only America's energy crisis, but also its pending
materials crisis.

Surface Mining Legislation

In spite of the fact that the United States is on the verge
of a second crisis, a minerals shortage, Congress is continuing to work on S. 425 and H.R. 11500, which deal with
and could do great harm to surface mining. The bill H.R.
11500 now under consideration by the House Interior
Committee contains what the American Mining Congress
considers major deficiencies.

The mining industry has not and does not oppose reasonable and realistic federal surface mining legislation; however, such legislation can only make a meaningful contribution to America's environmental and energy objectives if it
is firmly founded upon a conceptual understanding of the
basic relationship of the extractive industries to the viability of all other industries, including the other basic industry, agriculture. In analyzing H.R. 11500, the mining in-

dustry is convinced that the measure will lead to the prohibition of surface mining rather than to the regulation of reclamation activities. Many of its provisions will not only impede the necessary development and expansion of the country's domestic coal industry, but in too many instances the provisions would result in curtailment and elimination of currently producing operations—a result clearly not in line with the achievement of national energy self-sufficiency. Energy self-sufficiency by the end of this decade has been urged by many members of Congress and by former President Nixon in his announced program "Project Independence." Increased coal production is a key element to energy self-sufficiency, but, as written, H.R. 11500 would frustrate the achievement of the objectives of "Project Independence."

The following outline of major deficiencies is not all-inclusive, but demonstrates that H.R. 11500 would severely diminish the ability of the mining industry to respond to the nation's need for energy, without any real compensating environmental gains. The major conceptual deficiencies and the principal problem areas of concern are the following:

1. Environmental protection performance standards:
   a. Requiring backfilling to the "approximate original contour" fails to recognize that another contour may be equally as good or better for a desirable subsequent use.
   b. Continuing to put the requirements in terms of absolutes, which are not literally attainable, is not realistic.
   c. No consideration has yet been given to the cost-benefit ratio of a reclamation plan.
   d. The requirement for permanent establishment of

vegetative cover and a five- or ten-year monitoring requirement would prevent the production of winter wheat and row crops on reclaimed lands.

e. The special requirements for mining on steep slopes (those with a 20° or more rise) would essentially result in prohibition of mining on such slopes.

f. Criteria established for granting an exemption to open-pit operations from returning the site to its "approximate original contour" are so restrictive as to be virtually meaningless.

g. The criteria relating to protection against increases in dissolved solids are unrealistic and may prevent necessary action to neutralize acid runoff.

h. The proscription of mining within five hundred feet of abandoned mine openings is not appropriate and may prevent correction of environmental problems by "mining through."

2. Enforcement:

a. Except in the case of imminent danger to life and health, neither the secretary of the interior nor the state regulatory authority should have the power to order cessation of mining being conducted under a permit without resort to the judicial system.

b. Enforcement should be solely by means of state action so long as an approved state program is in effect.

c. The criminal penalty provisions are too broad and cover a multitude of acts for which they are not appropriate. Civil penalties should be assessed only by a court of law.

d. Too many opportunities for intervention and delay are afforded in the permit approval process and in the resultant operations under a permit. Review procedures should be streamlined to provide for both participation of those with legitimate legal interests and freedom of the applicant or permittee from repetitive reviews of the same issue.

e. The federal procurement proscription in section 603 is unnecessary in light of other enforcement provisions and is tantamount to "overkill."

f. Section 216 fails to specify grounds for suspension of a permit and does not set forth an appropriate procedure or proper grounds for revocation of a permit.

3. Designation of areas unsuitable for surface mining:

a. The provisions of section 205 and 501 actually establish a land use program and are inappropriate in surface mining legislation.

b. Any decision as to whether reclamation is physically or economically possible on a particular piece of land should be based only upon the permit application with respect to that land.

c. "Fragile or historic" land areas should be publicly acquired with just compensation paid to the owner.

d. Lands needed for essential governmental objectives should be acquired with government funds.

e. The prohibition against mining in a "renewable resource land area" is unrealistic. Minerals must be mined where they occur, and their mining should not be prohibited because they occur in "renewable resource" areas.

4. Permits and renewals:

a. The bill provides for the issuance of surface mining permits not to exceed five years' duration. There are no provisions for automatic renewal at the end of that time even though the operator may be in full compliance with the requirements of the act.

   b. The data required to be included as part of the permit application, as set forth in the bill, are better determined by the regulatory agency and should not be included in the legislation.

5. $2.50 per ton reclamation fee:

   a. Imposition of the fee is intended to "equalize" the costs of underground and surface mining to foster underground mining and thereby penalize surface mining. A credit against the fee, not to exceed 90 percent of the total fee, is allowed for certain health, safety, and reclamation expenses.

   b. The credit scheme provided not only tends to subsidize inefficiency, but also fails to account for costs already incurred for health and safety equipment purchased prior to possible enactment.

   c. The fee fails to account for the widely varying values of coal.

   d. The fee fails to account for the wide variations in the thickness of coal seams and the amount of coal which can be removed per acre of land disturbed by surface mining methods.

   e. The increased cost implicit in the $2.50 reclamation fee will further endanger the economics of coal gasification so desperately needed to supplement dwindling domestic natural gas supplies for household uses.

   f. The increased cost will undoubtedly cause serious delays in the development of new mines and the expansion of old mines, with a resultant delay in the essential expansion of coal production capacity.

g. The reclamation fee will seriously endanger realization of the national objectives embodied in "Project Independence."

6. Protection of the surface owner and water rights:

a. The bill inappropriately expands the rights of the surface owner vis-à-vis the mineral owner, where they are not one and the same, beyond existing and settled law by requiring the mineral owner to obtain the written consent of the surface owner to conduct surface mining operations. The bill should provide that in cases where the consent of the surface owner cannot be obtained, the operator may post a bond to cover damages to the surface owner.

b. The bill grants new proprietary rights for compensation to permittees and lessees of surface uses on federally owned lands, even though surface permits were issued subject to the right of the federal government to issue mineral leases and the mineral lessee has paid the government for the right to mine coal.

c. The bill could be interpreted so as to require the operator to acquire written permission or a waiver from the surface owner after the date of enactment, even though the operator has already acquired the necessary rights.

d. The bill interferes with established water law, which has been laboriously developed to govern water uses and can adequately protect water rights, by imposing the impossible burden of requiring the written consent of all owners of water rights and landowners "anticipated to be affected."

7. Inclusion of exploration activities:

a. The definition of surface mining operations in section 605 states that land areas "affected by exploration operations which substantially affect land surface" are within the coverage of the bill.

b. Inclusion of exploration operations as part of surface mining operations is confusing and unrealistic because the remainder of the bill and the procedures it would establish and contemplate deal specifically with only actual surface coal mining operations.

Land Use Planning Legislation

Land use bills pending in the House of Representatives cannot be considered balanced legislation. The findings, statements of policy, and the purpose regarding land use define laudable and important directions and goals and allude to many legitimate, important, and necessary land uses. The provisions of the bills, however, are tilted towards a single prevailing theme of environmental protection and concomitant prevention of land use and development.

Balanced and orderly use of land for basic human needs is neglected. The virtual veto power of the federal government, by withholding funds, over state land use plans is keyed to failure by the states to protect lands against environmental abuse. Other criteria are virtually nonexistent.

The mining industry welcomes the recognition of a need for improved and more efficient land use planning and decision making. However, it is important that legislation establishing a new land use planning system be carefully conceived, otherwise the purpose of the act may be frustrated by becoming a vehicle for imposing unsound land uses or, perhaps, nonuse. It is important that land use planning resulting from federal legislation not foreclose the extraction of minerals whenever it would best serve the interest of the nation.

Pending legislation, as now drafted, does not adequately recognize the unique nature of the use of land for mineral development. Likewise, it does not acknowledge the unique nature of mineral estates. For example, one provision requires each state to project the nature and quantity of land needed and suitable for each of a wide-ranging list of land uses, including mineral development. It is possible, although admittedly difficult, to make the projections for surface use such as transportation and urban development and most other uses. Only an educated guess could be used for a projection of the quantity of land needed for mineral development because, proportionately, small areas are actually required. Also, many possible mineral development needs are completely unknown. In Montana, for example, where mineral production is the second largest industry in the state, only 25,600 acres, or three one-hundredths of one percent of the total land area has been used in the history of the state for mineral production. Arizona, the largest producer of copper in the nation, has utilized slightly more than one-tenth of one percent of its land for mining. Only generalized estimates or guesses can be made of the number of acres of land which will probably be occupied for mineral development if this nation is to produce most of its mineral requirements. But to predetermine the geographic location of lands suitable for mineral development is an impossible legislative requirement. Except for operating mines and a few known undeveloped mineral occurrences, the location of lands suitable for mineral development is unknown and projections would be meaningless.

Many of the land use planning proposals would unnecessarily and arbitrarily limit the use of lands to specific purposes and would thereby seriously restrict the availability of lands for mineral exploration and development. We urge that all land use planning proposals and programs take cognizance of the unique nature of land use for mineral development. Proposals should recognize that mineral development can occur only where the minerals exist and many areas that may prove feasible for future mineral development cannot be identified at this time. Since the development of adequate domestic reserves of all mineral resources is of great national importance, we urge that land use programs specifically provide that mineral exploration and development not be impeded in the absence of a compelling public interest.

National Energy Research and Development Act of 1973

This bill was enacted in the Senate on December 7, 1973, by a vote of 82-0. A similar proposal was passed by the House on December 19, 1973. Some of the highlights of the Senate bill are:

1. The congressional findings have been supplemented to specifically state that at a minimum a national commitment to a ten-year, $20 billion energy research, development, and demonstration program is warranted by the urgency of national energy problems.
2. The statement of congressional policy has been revised to emphasize further the goal of national self-sufficiency through the use of domestic energy resources.
3. The statement of research priorities has been expanded and made more specific to provide congressional guidance for the preparation of a detailed strategy for federal support for energy research and development, to achieve solutions to (a) immediate and short-term (until

the early 1980s) energy and related environmental problems, (b) middle-term (1980s to 2000) problems, and (c) long-term (beyond 2000) problems.

4. Emphasis upon energy conservation research has been strengthened throughout the bill.

5. The congressional policy regarding potential forms of federal support for and participation with industry in demonstrations of new energy technologies has been expanded and made more specific.

6. The policies regarding patents arising out of research performed pursuant to the act have been made more flexible to reflect the diversity of possible cooperative research arrangements which may be forthcoming.

7. The bill provides for an independent program coordinated by the Council on Environmental Quality to carry out a continuing analysis of the adequacy of attention to energy conservation and environmental research under the provisions of this measure.

8. The specific authorizations of joint federal-industry corporations for the commercial demonstration of several energy technologies which were contained in Titles 2-6 of the bill as introduced have been deleted. Instead, the chairman of the Energy Management Project established by this measure would be authorized and directed to select the appropriate form of federal support for demonstrations and make recommendations to the Congress on a case-by-case basis. The joint corporation form could be selected, and a model structure for such a potential corporation is set forth in the bill.

The Senate also declared:

In the United States we now have for the first time very serious absolute shortages of natural gas, fuel oil, and other forms of energy as well as shortages of environmentally acceptable forms of energy. In the months ahead, many regions of the Nation will face critical shortages of heating fuel and gasoline.

These shortages are not caused by a lack of domestic energy resources. There are adequate domestic supplies of energy to meet all of our requirements for the foreseeable future. We have huge coal reserves in Appalachia and in the West. The oil shale deposits in the Western United States are an untapped energy resource of great potential. Geothermal power, the heat contained in the earth, could be a major source of energy. There are large volumes of oil and gas yet to be discovered on the Outer Continental Shelf in the United States.

The shortages we are experiencing and the shortages that all knowledgeable commentators project in the months ahead are the direct result of the Nation's failure to anticipate energy problems and to develop policies to deal with them. This is especially true in the area of energy research and development. We have failed to move from the realm of theory into the time of commercial demonstration.

Federal Energy Corporation Proposals

1. Oil and gas: an amendment, no. 643, to S. 2506 was offered by Senator Adlai Stevenson III which would establish a Federal Oil and Gas Corporation. During the hearings on the proposal, the American Mining Congress submitted the following:

It is our understanding that should the Federal Oil and Gas Corporation amendment be adopted it would authorize the federal government to engage directly in the full scope of exploration, production, transportation and refining of oil and gas on public and private lands. While the scope of this amendment does not relate to mining per se—which is the principal concern of the American Mining Congress—the suggested amendment nevertheless appears to us to be seriously at odds with the Mining and Minerals Policy Act of 1970 wherein the Congress declared it to be in the national interest to foster and encourage private enterprise in the development of an economically sound and stable minerals industry. As described within the Act, minerals have been defined to include all minerals and mineral fuels including oil, gas, coal, oil shale and uranium.

We believe that the government corporation called for in amendment No. 643 is incompatible with our American private enterprise system. While industry recognizes the absolute need for government assistance in research, we are concerned about considerable federal involvement in the internal decision-making process of private industry. Commercial production of oil and gas by government companies is particularly disturbing. We strongly oppose such entry by the government into direct substantial competition with its taxpayers of the private business sector.

. . . [A main] cause of our energy problem is primarily the failure of public policies, particularly in not recognizing the need for proper incentives to develop energy resources and in not reconciling conflicting goals of society.

. . . [It should be noted that] the American private enterprise system contains a diverse range of resources, technologies and managerial skills which are readily available and which can be blended to solve the many complex energy problems confronting the nation. This private enterprise system is a proven vehicle which has and will continue to best serve this nation in meeting the needs of its citizenry. The American system of free enterprise as such should be fostered and encouraged, not inhibited. Regrettably the sure result of an amendment like No. 643 would be to severely debilitate this system.

In summary, the American Mining Congress respectfully requests that in your deliberations on S. 2506, and more specifically on amendment No. 643, that your Committee (1) adhere to the policies set forth in the Mining and Minerals Policy Act of 1970, and (2) carefully avoid any enactment that would impede the private enterprise system.

2. Oil shale (H.R. 12014): this proposal, introduced on December 18, 1973, would amend the Mineral Leasing Act to provide for a public corporation to explore and develop oil shale energy resources on federal lands. No action has as yet been taken on this proposal.

Amendments to the Federal Mineral Leasing Laws

As noted above, there are proposals in the present Congress, as there have been proposals before Congress in the past, which would repeal the Mining Law of 1872 and place locatable minerals under a leasing system.

If such proposed legislation is enacted the American Mining Congress believes that it would discourage rather than encourage mineral exploration and development. The Mining Congress continues to endorse its previously proposed Mineral Development Act, which adopts most of the Land Law Review Commission's recommendations on mining law revision and which would deal effectively with the criticisms which have been made of the existing general mining laws. This recommendation would simplify administration of the public land laws and the mining laws, facilitate multiple use of the public lands, and accommodate the increasing use and demands for such lands. While providing for the needs of the public-land-managing agencies and protection of the environment, it preserves those rights which are essential if private enterprise is to continue to develop· America's domestic mineral resources, viz., access to the public lands for exploration, location and development of mineral resources, and security of tenure to develop the resources. The proposal would make it clear that exploration and mining activities under the mining law are not exempt for the applicable laws and regulations relating to the protection of the environment.

I have only touched in detail on some of the pending legislative proposals that would directly affect the minerals producing industry. I have not attempted to cover even briefly several other existing new laws which directly affect the mining industry, such as the mine safety laws, environmental statutes, and the Water Pollution Control Act, as well as numerous other enactments which bear on mining.

These latter laws are now in the process of being interpreted in the form of administrative regulations, as well as by the courts. It behooves all concerned with mining operations here in the United States and abroad to acquaint themselves with the pending legislation noted above, as well as the laws, regulations, and court decisions covering the newly enacted laws just noted. Having done so it becomes crystal clear that the minerals industry is indeed in a new ball game both in the United States and abroad.

3

C. *Thomas Houseman*

Future Mineral Supplies: An Economic and Financial Perspective

Many of the basic mineral resource problems that must be met today and in the future are concerned with the utilization and flow of money. I will present some thoughts and ideas on the economic and financial implications of mineral supply problems. My objective is to put mineral resources and their utilization in perspective with world trade, economic growth, and national goals.

It has frequently been stated that the first step in coping with a problem is recognizing that one exists. There must be few people indeed in the United States at this moment who are not aware that the country has a mineral supply problem, even though the causes and the ultimate extent or impact are not exactly crystal clear. There exists a short-term threat to America's economy, comfort, and pattern of living. How does the nation's mineral situation relate to that of other countries, industrialized and under-developed? Can other raw-material-producing nations emulate the oil producers in exercising price and supply control? Does the world face an absolute raw materials shortage or is there availability at a price?

Listen to what the experts say:

1. Some quarters, most notably the so-called Club of

47

Rome, have warned of severe shortages of metals and minerals by the end of this century.

2. A study by Canada's Department of Energy, Mines and Resources concludes that the danger to the world lies not in the lack of minerals but in their availability. It says that if new technologies are used to recover nonrenewable resources in large quantities, irreparable damage will be done to renewable resources such as air, soil, and water.

3. Fred Bergsten of the Brookings Institute believes that groups of raw material producers now have the capability to form cartels controlling a number of commodities and to dictate political and economic conditions to the industrialized countries.

4. Philip Trezise, also of Brookings, believes it is ridiculous to translate what the oil countries have done into what bauxite or tin or copper producers might do. He concludes the latter are poor countries without the financial strength to effectively withhold commodities from world markets.

5. Both the *Economist* and the *Mining Journal* in London make a case that, rather than shortages, a greater threat to world economies is the real possibility of metal and mineral surpluses. If there is a rush to develop known resources domestically or in countries considered politically safe, sizable short-term oversupply could result.

What is apparent is that, no matter which view of the situation one is emotionally or intellectually inclined to hold, he can find support for his position. This presents a dilemma to government and corporate policy makers on a worldwide scale. The concept of rational planning becomes baseless when rational men reach so many different answers on fundamental questions.

I believe that the concern in the United States should be

where the country stands in regard to its mineral supply needs relative to the rest of the world, and where other nations stand relative to America and to each other. As the title of this chapter suggests, let's put some things in perspective. Interior Secretary Rogers C. B. Morton correctly pointed out in 1973 in his annual report to Congress, "Energy and minerals are the lifeblood of our industrial economy, and development of our domestic resources is not keeping pace with our needs." This is certainly true in an absolute sense. However, it is also true for every other industrialized country, and most are far worse off for domestic resources than is the United States.

Whether in the future we become more reliant on our domestic resources or on imports may not be the principal problem facing us. I think it is necessary for producers and consumers to undertake a continuous study of every commodity that is significant in world trade and vital to world economic health and growth. The existence of resources, their availability, and their consumption must be viewed in terms of today's economics and technology. Their potential availability and consumption must be evaluated assuming different technologic and economic conditions.

The threat of shortages must be defined as to the nature of the shortage. Is there an absolute lack of resources or can it, in reality, be a shortage in productive capacity? Is there availability at a price? Can a shortage be contrived for purposes of immediate political or economic gain? How long might a shortage last? How can it be countered over the short and long term? Concern should be balanced with the certain knowledge that substantial changes in availability and price bring into play forces that tend to limit the process.

Since the oil crisis is currently the focus of much of the

world's attention, let's consider a few of its ramifications.

The strength and diversity of the United States economy and the economies of numerous other industrial powers give them the flexibility to adapt to changing forces over a period of time. It is the suddenness of a major event such as the oil cutback and price increases that can cause real economic disruption.

The combination of a business recession and inflation are virtually a foregone conclusion in 1974 for the countries that make up the Organization of Economic Cooperation and Development, the United States, Canada, Japan, and the nations of western Europe. Inflation averaged nearly 10 percent in these countries in 1973 and may climb into the teens in 1974. A business contraction is likely to ensue because of energy shortages. This may be accompanied by the diversion of funds to oil purchases that would have been otherwise employed. A problem with more unpredictable consequences and uncertain remedies is the skyrocketing balance of payments deficit for the O.E.C.D. countries. Large deficits could lead to a spiral of competitive and mutually frustrating actions such as devaluation, trade restrictions, and competitive interest rate escalation.

For the so-called third-world countries, the effects of energy problems, inflation, or recession are almost certain to be more severe and long-lasting. A recent World Bank study analyzed their plight this way:

Oil in the less developed countries is used mainly for industry, electric power, and public transportation. There is little cushion of luxury consumption to be cut back. To the extent less oil is imported, due to unavailability or excessive cost, economic activity will be reduced.

Because of higher prices, there will be less foreign exchange to spend on other imports, such as food, fertilizers, and capital goods needed for development. Because of the economic slowing in the industrial countries, purchases from the poor countries will decline, further impairing their foreign exchange reserves. All of these factors constitute a radical change in the outlook for underdeveloped economies.

The effect of the oil situation on the oil-exporting countries that precipitated the crisis is also a subject of considerable interest. As a result of the price increases, the petroleum-exporting countries will soon be the recipients of such an enormous transfer of currency that they may not be able to accommodate it. The total of these countries' revenues from oil is expected to reach between $80 and $105 billion this year. Their capacity to absorb goods and services, however, is thought unlikely to exceed $30 to $35 billion, leaving an incredible unspent surplus of $50 to $70 billion.

There are a number of outlets for this unspent surplus. Some of it could be converted into gold or other metals. Some of it could be invested directly in securities or industrial enterprises in other countries. The bulk of it, however, will probably flow into the existing pool of Eurodollars, American dollars stranded abroad by previous foreign investment restrictions.

According to most estimates, there are now about $110 billion Eurodollars in circulation. But in just two years, this figure could be doubled by the flow of oil dollars. This money will be seeking investment and lending opportunities around the world. At the same time, there will be a scramble for funds by prospective borrowers from countries whose credit-worthiness has been weakened most by the oil crisis.

It will take considerable ingenuity on the part of central

banks and private financial institutions to match these surpluses and shortages of funds. If it can't be done smoothly, there is a great risk of competitive devaluations, exchange restrictions, and currency speculation, thereby worsening the prospects for reasonable and balanced world economic growth.

Problems and uncertainties brought on by the oil crisis are causing wisespread doubts in the United States about the reliability of foreign mineral supplies. The fact that the country is a net importer of minerals is also viewed with alarm because of the impact of its balance of trade.

It's possible that these worries will induce the government to encourage a more rapid development and greater reliance on domestic resources. There would be obvious benefits from such a policy. But there are also risks in building too great a dependence on our own production. We have seen recurring instances of industries being shut down or economically weakened by the actions of labor and by legislated environmental controls. The United Kingdom is in a desperate situation for energy at this time because of overdependence on two sources: the Arab countries for oil and a single, nationalized industry for coal.

Maybe the best, long-term national security for a continuing stable supply of vital mineral materials can be attained by having a dispersed source of supply with a considerable spread of control. This could ensure maximum competition and a minimum opportunity for monopoly.

The argument that we need a favorable balance of trade in minerals can be misleading. In my opinion, it is not relevant to match up imports and exports of similar commodities in looking at trade surplus or deficit. Only the total balance is significant.

Consider the performance of Japan over the last several years. From the recession year of 1965, Japan's GNP grew from $88 billion to $300 billion. Real growth during this period was 10.8 percent per year. Exports rose from $8.3 billion to $28 billion, imports from $6.4 to $19.1 billion, and the net trade surplus therefore from $1.9 to $8.9 billion. Of the total imports in 1972, raw materials and mineral fuels made up 55 percent. Without importing $3.5 billion of steelmaking materials and nonferrous ores, it is obvious that Japan could not have exported more than $10 billion worth of metal products, motor vehicles, and ships. The Japanese have been more concerned with availability, price, and efficient utilization of raw materials than with a net mineral trade balance.

Despite its much greater dependence on mineral imports than America's, Japan has consistently outperformed the United States in both economic growth and trade surplus.

It's fair to ask whether the oil supply and price squeeze will bring the Japanese miracle to an end. The current mineral situation demonstrates the risk that accompanies dependence on foreign supplies. Certainly the suddenness and dimension of the oil squeeze has shocked Japan, but it has been aware for some time of the vulnerability of its success formula. Japan's response has been to expand its overseas involvement. Japanese investment abroad has been growing in both the natural resource and manufacturing sectors. Current Japanese overseas investment is about $10 billion, up by $3 billion in the past year. By 1980 a $27 billion total is expected, and about half of this will be in natural resources. Significantly, by 1980, more than 25 percent of total Japanese investment in manufacturing will be outside of Japan.

Certainly, however, Japan's basic resource position is vastly different from America's. The United States has domestic resources to develop and Japan does not.

The principal point I'd like to make is that national policies must have a balanced approach to strategic, social, economic, and political considerations. A nation must strive to make the most effective use of its strengths, whether these be in agriculture, minerals, energy, technology, or whatever. If a nation must import certain goods, then it must export certain goods to survive in the international community. A national minerals policy, or agriculture policy, or energy policy, or trade policy cannot be drawn up in isolation. It must fit the broader needs of the nation.

A strong minerals position by itself is not a guarantee of economic strength. By and large, the mineral-exporting countries are and have been relatively poor. If the world is really entering an era of mineral shortages, either real or contrived, then prices will rise. Unless mineral prices increase relative to the price increases of agricultural and manufactured goods, however, there will be no net gain for the producer countries. The oil-exporting nations have effected such a relative price increase, at least for now. The impact on them as well as on the rest of the world over the next few years will either provide or remove the incentive for other groups of mineral commodity producers to undertake similar courses of action.

4

C. H. Burgess

Mineral Resources, Productive Capacity, and Related Problems: An Industry Point of View

Many of those persons who are concerned with minerals believe that their importance to man has not been fully appreciated by the consuming public. The great wealth of the United States in mineral as well as other resources has been taken for granted. Although it has been acknowledged as a vague abstraction that some of them were not renewable and disappeared in use, the total quantity was deemed to be so great that as a practical matter the public did not have to worry about the future.

On the other hand, numerous individual experts and institutions have attempted to measure the adequacy of supply to meet the projected demand for various mineral commodities and have made recommendations for public action. The annual reports of the secretary of the interior under the Mining and Minerals Policy Act of 1970 and the Final Report of the National Commission on Materials Policy published in June 1973 provide comprehensive analyses.

The current anxiety concerning the hard minerals has been triggered by the action of the Arab states with respect to petroleum. A spate of pronouncements on hard

55

main lacking a mineral discovery of ore which would be commercial at present.

Authoritative figures on exploration expenditures are hard to obtain and those that are available are often compiled using different accounting bases. Some cost data comprise exploration only, some include work on or near operating mines, and still others probably embrace some mine development as well as exploration. Using the best material available to me, and making guesses where data are lacking, I estimate the annual budget for hard mineral exploration by private concerns, worldwide, at somewhere between $200 million and $300 million. Search carried out by governments and by the United Nations would be additional.

In rare cases exploration may turn up a great deposit which can be seen at a very early stage to be not only viable but highly profitable. In many instances, however, successful development is deferred for years pending solution of technological, marketing, legal, or other problems. I would like to cite several illustrations.

The Ecstall mine of Texas Gulf Sulphur in Ontario is a splendid property that was put into production promptly after discovery of the orebody. Exploration was based on a hypothesis of ore occurrence, not on showings in outcrop, and was conducted over a period of four years at a cost of about $3 million. Sixty-five geophysical anomalies were drilled in succession and proved to be duds before the sixty-sixth yielded a thick intercept of high-grade mineralization in an area which had been intensively explored over a number of years because of its propinquity to other important mining districts. Drilling of the orebody was carried out beginning April 1, 1964, and stripping began in the fall of that same year. Production got under way in

1966. Total costs to time of start-up were $85 million. Abundant publicity on the richness of this discovery conveyed the impression to thousands that bonanzas are easy to come by, but the long history of frustration in exploration is much less widely appreciated, and is rarely published.

Taconite was long known in Minnesota but was of no economic interest while the high-grade merchantable iron ore was available in vast quantities. The first large tracts of taconite-bearing land were put together with a view to mining some sixty years ago. In the 1920s an attempt to produce iron concentrates on a commercial scale was a financial failure. Subsequently, with the development of thermal jet piercing for blast hole drilling and changes in blast furnace practices and in the economics of the iron ore market, taconite has become a profitable and important mineral product.

Copper production from the Lone Star mining district in the Gila Mountains near Safford, Arizona, was first recorded in 1886, but output has been negligible. In 1949 one group spent over $200,000 in exploration drilling but gave up because of poor vlaues. Several years later hundreds of square miles were staked and explored by several companies. Phelps Dodge acquired claims in 1957 and started exploration. They recently announced the appropriation of an additional $30 million toward development, bringing the total expenditure to date to $44.4 million.

The Henderson orebody in Colorado was found in a long-known district in 1965, construction began two years later, and to the end of 1973 more than $127 million had been spent in development. Production is scheduled for 1977, at which time it is estimated that total expenditures will have exceeded $300 million.

The great Bougainville deposit was discovered in the 1960s and the extent of the orebody determined by drilling through 1968. The mine was brought into production in 1973 at a cost of $470 million. The Ertsberg orebody in West Irian, New Guinea, was first examined by Freeport Minerals in 1960, but a contract of work was not executed until 1967. It started to produce in 1973 after the expenditure of $175 million.

It is one thing to review such projects after they have been completed and launched into successful operation. It is quite a different perspective beforehand when there remain many unknowns and doubts as to whether the undertaking will ever pan out. An example is the copper-nickel mineralization in the Duluth Gabbro in Minnesota. The values were first discovered in interesting quantity in 1948. By now, a quarter of a century later, expenditures in exploration and testing probably aggregate something in the order of $7 to $8 million. Some work is continuing, and there is a possibility that this potential may be realized, but in the meanwhile it remains a resource and not an ore reserve.

Considerable interest has attended work in recent years on the manganese nodules in the oceans. Samples were first dredged up more than one hundred years ago by the *Challenger,* a British oceanographic vessel, in the course of a cruise around the world, but no likelihood of commercial potential was taken seriously until the 1960s. The deposits which appear to·be most promising lie three miles deep in the Pacific Ocean. Their study required new approaches.

Obtaining samples by dredging is a slow procedure and very costly because of the large charges for ship time. Photography of the ocean bed and, to a much lesser extent, television have been used for scanning for nodules.

The task of exploration was, therefore, unique and had not previously been carried out. The composition and structure of the nodules are likewise unique. The efficient extraction of the metals will require novel methods of treatment. Gathering and lifting the nodules to a ship at the surface for transport to a treatment plant are tasks that had never been performed and a challenge to engineering. The principal metals to be recovered—nickel and copper— occur in the nodules at a ratio very different from the ratio of current consumption so that a large output from this source could have an important impact in nickel economy and much less in copper. Although there is at present no legal prohibition against mining nodules on a commercial scale, neither is there any international or world legal regime sponsored by a responsible government authority that can guarantee exclusivity over a mining area and provide legal protection against interference by another party of different nationality.

During the last dozen years, however, great progress has been made. Samples have been taken from thousands of stations, many of them with a free-fall device which is much more rapid than the dredging operation previously used. The quantities, distribution, and assay content have been determined, and discrete deposits delineated. Studies of bottom conditions have progressed. A great deal of experimental work has been done on the means of lifting nodules to the surface. Metallurgical schemes have been devised and tested in pilot runs. The United Nations has given increasing attention to a legal regime; the United States Congress is considering bills concerned with this subject.

Several groups from several nations are now at work on the exploration and processing of manganese nodules. One consortium consisting of companies of four nationalities has recently announced a research and development program estimated to exceed $50·million during the next few years. If the outcome of this work and other conditions for operations prove to be favorable, a commercial undertaking might be launched on the scale of 10,000 tons of nodules a day. The capital cost of such an undertaking is estimated to be about $250 million, and the annual output of nickel and copper would be in the neighborhood of 45,000 tons and 35,000 tons, respectively. I estimate expenditures to the present date on the manganese nodules by American and foreign concerns at something over $90 million and the present annual rate at about $20 million. If commercial production of metals from nodules should begin in the early 1980s, it will be after two decades of work and an expenditure of more than $200 million prior to the decision to enter into commercial production.

Knowledge of the history of such undertakings is essential to an understanding by the nation's legislators of the nature of mineral resource development.

Turning now to mineral imports, we find that the Arab embargo on oil has created concern lest developing countries that produce hard minerals follow the Arab lead. Prominently mentioned are the CIPEC countries—Chile, Peru, Zaire, and Zambia—which are the leading exporters of copper. Their production is 36 percent of the world's total. There is much speculation about the likelihood of an embargo or price squeeze by the CIPEC countries. It would seem very difficult for these four countries—which are so heavily dependent on exports of the metal for foreign exchange and indeed for such a large portion of their domestic economy—to forego all income from this source, particularly in view of the fact that they lack the great foreign exchange balances of the Arabs. It should be recognized that the economics of production of petroleum and of metals are very different and that those differences affect the opportunity to use these commodities for political ends. Exploration costs are high for both oil and metals, but when oil is found, production costs are low per unit value of product compared to metals and the number of workers required is much lower. The payout of investment is much more rapid in oil than in, say, copper, where return of capital is normally achieved after several years of operation which may represent a considerable part of the life of the mine. If for a moment we assume a basic production cost for Mideast oil, excluding taxes, royalty, and so on, of thirty cents a barrel, and that same figure for a pound of copper, it is evident that the going sale price of the oil is an order of magnitude greater than this production cost, but in the case of the copper, it is only two or three times as large. Withholding copper by leaving it in the ground would entail large unemployment with consequent social and financial dislocation. To produce and stockpile copper would require and immobilize large sums of working capital with no assurance that the metal could later be sold without loss. Substitution of other materials for copper must be taken into account also.

Nonetheless, the issue of self-sufficiency in hard minerals has been sharpened by the Arab oil experience, and there is much talk of reducing our reliance on foreign sources for many minerals by increasing domestic production.

Current anxiety may represent an overreaction. The changeover from proclaimed interdependence to economic warfare may not yet have arrived. The present urgency to become self-sufficient shows little evidence of concern for long-term strategy. I have not heard any recognition that, thanks to America's use of cheaper foreign oil in these past decades, it has more left in the ground today. (Note that several of the Arab states have reversed their long-term policy of increasing production capacity further and further, in order to conserve their reserves.)

Man has used more minerals—including petroleum—in the past thirty years than in all previous time, we are told. The United States has produced and consumed a disproportionately large share. While America is still in a continuing phase of acceleration of consumption, is it prudent to accelerate even further the depletion of its remaining deposits for the objective of self-sufficiency, thereby leaving a freer hand in the world market for other industrial competitor nations? Even at some risk of the country's overseas mineral supply, would it be better in the long run—fifty years or a hundred in the future—to continue production from America's deposits at a normal rate, paying for the imports with the nation's great, renewable, agricultural wealth? These questions should be considered by United States policy makers.

Paradoxical though it might seem, the United States imports a substantial part of its needs of some metals of which it has large domestic reserves, including iron and zinc. The reason, of course, is that the foreign material is cheaper. If all of the imported materials were to be replaced with domestic—insofar as possible—some price or other incentive would be required to compensate the producer for the higher costs and risks involved. Present difficulties of the mining industry would be exacerbated. The present laws · and regulations and proposed changes concerning land use and tenure, strip mining, health and safety, pollution abatement, environmental constraints, all of which have raised costs in recent years and in some cases shut down operations, would apply to the new production facilities, of course, and give rise to escalated costs.

I opened this chapter with the observation that many economic geologists believe that the importance of minerals to man has not been appreciated by the consuming public. Their importance is clearly recognized by some governments of countries which produce them. Marketing of mineral exports is tightly controlled by many governments, as in the case of copper in Chile, and vigorously monitored, if that is the correct phrase, in the case of coal and iron in Australia. The importance of mineral supply—chiefly from abroad—to Japan, Germany, and France, for example, is reflected in their governments' financial assistance to their nationals exploring for and developing orebodies overseas.

Official and public appreciation in the United States of the need for minerals is probably keener now than it has ever been before. Economic geologists should do what they can to enlighten America's policy makers and their fellow citizens on mineral-related topics where they have expertise. Accurate, factual information is essential to the development of sound mineral policies.

5   *Eugene N. Cameron*

Alternatives
for Survival

The title of this chapter requires some explanation, and a definition. The term *survival* implies the existence of some threat of extinction, but although man has been in possession of the means of his own extinction for some time, his survival as a species on this planet is not the issue to which this symposium is addressed. What we really are discussing is the survival of a way of life in America, a way of life that is the culmination of centuries of effort to improve the material aspects of our existence. The success of that effort during the past century has been based on an increasing scale of use of minerals, both as sources of energy and as raw materials. So the question becomes simply this: can the United States maintain the flow of minerals that it would like to have in order to support or perhaps even improve its present material standard of living?

Which course of action will best assure us of the necessary mineral supplies? Is there really a choice, or is there open to us only a single course of action, already fixed by factors beyond our control? Are there, indeed, alternatives for survival?

A full answer to this last question would require examination of a broad spectrum of economic, social, and political problems, many of them beyond the scope of a mere geologist like myself. But any alternatives for survival that deserve serious consideration must be consistent with the nature and distribution of the mineral resources of the United States and of the world, and it is from this standpoint that the economic geologist may speak.

For the United States the first basis of any alternative for survival is the nature, the size, and the economic and technological availability of its mineral resources. We have much information on this subject—estimates of known reserves and resources of various minerals, data for domestic mineral production and consumption of minerals, and forecasts of future production and consumption to the end of the twentieth century. We have these largely as a result of massive efforts on the part of the U.S. Geological Survey and the U.S. Bureau of Mines. Their data are the basis of the recent report of the National Materials Policy Commission.

The data are not perfect, because the quality and completeness of information available to the compilers of the report were not uniform for all minerals. Nor do the estimates tell us what rates and costs of production can be expected from known reserves. Nevertheless, the data are the foundation of all forecasts of our mineral future.

Now forecasts of the shape of mineral things to come lack the precision of the astronomer's prediction of the next eclipse. For minerals there are no firm predictions. Mineral forecasts, despite attempts to take into account such factors as technological developments, exploration for new mineral resources, and economic and population growth, are primarily projections of past trends. Usually they tell us what we may expect if our future course of action is a continuation of our actions in the past.

Despite all these uncertainties and imperfections, both

data and forecasts are extremely valuable, nay indispensable, for at least they give us baselines from which we can survey possibilities for the future. On occasion, they speak to us of things we should not do. Unfortunately, we do not always listen. The petroleum forecasts of the last few years are a case in point—perhaps "sore point" would be more apt.

Dr. Morgan has reviewed the present mineral position of the United States in chapter 1. It is a strong position. Any nation that produces more than 80 percent of all the minerals it consumes looks to the future from a position of strength, not weakness. Of all the advanced industrial nations of the world, only Soviet Russia surpasses the United States in the size and diversity of its mineral resources relative to its needs, and none of the other nations can approach America in this respect. But, as Dr. Morgan has pointed out, there are significant elements of weakness in the nation's present mineral position.

What about the forecasts for the period to the end of the century? When we examine them, we find that there is substantial agreement among them on certain salient points:

1. The United States can continue to be an important producer of minerals, both minerals for energy and minerals for raw materials, and can continue to produce a major share of the mineral materials that it requires.

2. United States production of petroleum, natural gas, and certain essential mineral raw materials, now insufficient to meet its needs, will be increasingly insufficient as we approach the end of the century. Apart from petroleum and natural gas, the metals are the severest problem: the ferroalloys except molybdenum, the nonferrous

metals, especially aluminum and tin, and the precious metals.

3. Discoveries of new deposits of the kinds we currently use are unlikely to reverse or seriously modify the trend toward increasing inadequacy of supplies of metals from domestic sources.

4. A burgeoning world demand means increasing competition for mineral supplies in world markets.

All forecasts I have seen make these four points. There is an additional point, however, that is not included in any of the forecasts that I have seen but should be included in them. It is this: as the mineral self-sufficiency of the United States declines, there will be a gradual movement abroad of industry based on the deficient minerals. This point was brought out long ago by D. F. Hewett, in an article on "Cycles in Metal Production" in the AIME *Transactions* for 1929. Mineral industry, over the long term, tends to move toward the sources of mineral raw materials. The movement of smelting, refining, and processing industries toward the sources of raw materials is now being encouraged by governments in virtually every mineral-producing country of the world. The effects of this are already being felt in the United States. The movement of American ferroalloy industry abroad has been underway for some time. The first stage of transfer of the American aluminum industry is apparently in progress. As shown in Figure 5.1, United States imports of bauxite have leveled off, but net imports of alumina, that is, imports minus exports, have been rising almost steadily since 1966. The reason is that the processing of bauxite to obtain alumina, the first stage in the production of aluminum metal, is being done more and more in the bauxite-pro-

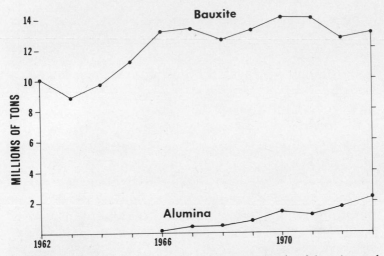

Figure 5.1. Net imports (imports minus exports) of bauxite and alumina, 1962-73. Data from U.S. Department of the Interior, Bureau of Mines, *Commodity Data Summaries,* annual issues (Pittsburgh, Pa.: The bureau, 1964-74).

ducing countries. The geographic distribution of new aluminum smelters planned or under construction suggests that further shifts involving the smelting and refining stages can be expected in the future.

Now most recent forecasts are predicated on the assumption that the United States will take the same basic approach to the problem of mineral supply that it has taken in the past. That approach is implicit, for example, in the forecasts contained in the First Report of the Secretary of the Interior under the Mining and Materials Policy Act of 1970, and in the analysis presented with the June 1974 report of the National Materials Policy Commission. The cardinal recommendation of the commission's report is "that traditional economic policy be maintained by relying upon market forces as the prime determinant of the mix of imports and domestic production subject to considerations of public policy involving the national security, health, and viability of domestic materials industries, and fair competition." Despite the qualifications, the recommendation is, basically, that we continue to treat the problem of mineral supply in the same way as in the past.

The course of action recommended by the Materials Policy Commission is predicated on three assumptions:

1. That the United States will continue to have access to the world's mineral supplies. At the present time, the United States is drawing significant portions of its mineral supplies from thirty-odd countries of the world. In the face of growing inadequacies of United States mineral production, the problem of access presumably will be broader and more complex in the future. For decades the United States has had access to world mineral supplies largely through the efforts of American industry in developing mineral resources abroad. This system is steadily breaking down, hence some new system of access presumably must be found. Continued access to mineral supplies, however, is the first assumption.

2. The second assumption is that the mineral production of the world will keep pace not only with the increasing mineral requirements of the United States, but with the exponential growth of world populations and the efforts of other nations to improve their material standards of living.

3. The third assumption is that the United States will find the means to pay for increased mineral imports.

Only experience can tell whether these assumptions are valid. Perhaps this is a risk that we must take. But assump-

tions are only assumptions, and in this case the stakes of
the game of mineral policy are extremely high. Is there no
alternative to the global dependence that is the inevitable
consequence of the mineral policies of the past? It would
seem prudent at this point at least to consider some
alternative to the policy that has been proposed. The
United States is currently absorbing a sharp lesson in the
consequences of undue dependence on foreign sources for
vital mineral supplies. This seems an appropriate time to
recognize potentially similar situations with respect to
certain metals for which there are serious deficiencies in
United States production.

Is there an alternative? I think there is, but to develop it
we must examine the basis of our past treatment of the
mineral problem. I use the phrase "treatment of the mineral problem" rather than the words "mineral policy,"
because to me a "mineral policy" means a series of measures that are adopted with reference to carefully thought
out national goals and are part of a comprehensive plan
aimed at achieving these goals. If the United States has
ever had a mineral policy in this sense, except during two
world conflicts, I am not aware of it.

It seems to me that our past treatment of the mineral
problem, and the policy proposed by the Materials Policy
Commission, rest on two basic principles. One principle is
the application of a particular concept of the problem of
minerals supply. According to this concept, the mineral
supply problem is that of meeting whatever demands for
minerals are created by a rapidly expanding and increasingly versatile technology. If a new product is developed,
mineral raw materials must be found. Whether or not the
mineral raw materials are available from domestic sources
is irrelevant. If domestic mines cannot furnish the min-

erals, then they must be sought from sources abroad. Under this concept of the problem of mineral supply, demand for minerals is controlled by technology. That is the first principle. The second principle is that reliance should be placed, in the words of the National Materials Policy Commission, "upon market forces as the prime determinant of the mix of imports and domestic production . . . ."

In my judgment it is the pursuit of these principles in the past that has led to the present mineral position of the United States. If the United States continues to pursue these principles, and if growth of the American economy continues, the forecasts of the country's future mineral position will be confirmed.

The first principle, control of demand by technology, is the more basic one, for it automatically leads to inadequacy of domestic mineral supplies. It has long since been demonstrated that so long as demand is technology-controlled, self-sufficiency in minerals is impossible for the United States. One has only to match the current demands of technology against United States mineral reserves and resources to see that self-sufficiency is impossible now or in the foreseeable future, so long as technology controls demand for minerals.

What about these two principles? Are they the only principles on which a mineral policy can be constructed? I do not think so. In fact, I think that if we discard these principles, an alternative for survival lies before us.

Since we can no longer tailor domestic mineral supply to the demands of technology, and if the consequences of trying to do so are unacceptable, then why not tailor our technology, so far as possible, to the availability of minerals from domestic sources? There is no natural law that requires that demand be technology-controlled. Second, why should the United States allow market forces to be the prime determinant of its mineral supply? The energy problem is an example of what happens when we do this. There are huge energy resources in the United States, but it has been easier to go after cheap petroleum and natural gas both at home and abroad than to learn to use our far larger resources of coal and oil shale, not to mention fissionable materials, economically and acceptably. Can we now afford the easy course? Increased imports of oil were a palliative, not a cure. They were a postponement of an evil day, at the price of insecurity and increased difficulties with our international balance of trade. They have retarded research and development of our own large energy resources, and they have helped set the stage for our current energy crisis. The same is true for certain of our deficient metals.

Under the alternative, United States technology would be controlled primarily by the availability of minerals from domestic sources, and market forces would no longer be the prime determinant of a mix of imports and domestic production. American technology and industry would be directed toward making maximum use of the nation's most abundant minerals, toward eliminating use of as many deficient minerals as possible, and toward minimizing use of the remaining deficient minerals.

I am sure that many will be appalled at the suggestion of this alternative. At first hearing it raises the specter of the disappearance of huge segments of American technology and industry. But is that really inevitable? The United States has never made a national effort to adapt its technology to its mineral resources. Given the scientific, financial, and technological resources of this country, is it really impossible to achieve this goal, or at least to make such progress toward it that the trend toward increased dependence on global resources can be arrested, perhaps even reversed?

I find considerable encouragement in an examination of the nature of the country's mineral deficiencies, both present and as forecast for the future. The major deficiencies are expressed in Figure 5.2, which is based on data of the Bureau of Mines and compares deficits in 1970 with deficits forecast for 1985.

The largest deficits, both actual and forecast, are in the fuels, in iron and in aluminum. There is no disagreement on our fuel resources. We have ample resources for a long time to come, if we develop the means of utilizing them economically and acceptably.

United States reserves of iron ore are ample for the country's needs to the end of the century. Resources available at somewhat higher cost are enormous.

United States reserves of bauxite are small, but resources of aluminum in high-alumina clays, anorthosite, alunite, and dawsonite are essentially unlimited. The problem, again, is to learn to use them economically and with acceptable impact on the environment.

United States reserves and resources of copper are large. They are potentially adequate for a long period if the proper economic and legal framework for development of known deposits and discovery of new deposits is provided, and if conservation in the use of copper is practiced. After nearly seventy years of lip service to the cause of mineral conservation, and nearly seventy years of living with vague though lofty definitions of the term, perhaps it is time we came to grips with the real problems of mineral conservation.

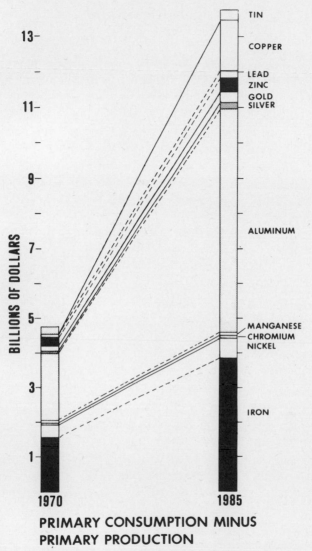

Figure 5.2. United States deficiencies in fuels and principal deficiencies in metals, in 1970 dollars, actual for 1970, forecast for 1985. Data from J. D. Morgan, Jr., "Future Use of Minerals: The Question of Demand," in *The Mineral Position of the United States*, ed. E. N. Cameron (Madison: The University of Wisconsin Press, 1973).

What is true of copper is true of lead and zinc. United States reserves of the two metals are among the largest in the world. The potential for discovery of additional reserves is high. Economic, political, and environmental problems, however, must be resolved.

United States resources of manganese are low in grade relative to present commercial standards and most of the known deposits present metallurgical problems. Resources, however, are very large. An alternative is recourse to the nodules of the ocean floors.

United States reserves of nickel and cobalt are small, but large resources of nickel are contained in the Duluth complex. In addition, access to sea floor nodules could remedy our deficiencies in both metals.

Chromium is a severe problem, and an effort would have to be made to reduce its use and to find ways of utilizing very low-grade resources to satisfy the most essential needs.

Silver and gold are special cases. Conservation in use seems the only solution. Surely there are more essential uses than hoarding and the production of sets of medals dedicated to Jonathan Livingston Seagull.

There are problems with the metals on this list. There are problems in obtaining minerals and metals that are not on this list. Many of these are used in no large amounts, but nonetheless they play essential roles in current technology and industry. But how many of these problems would disappear if a massive effort of research, redesign, and redevelopment were undertaken and pursued vigorously over an adequate period of time?

The alternative I have outlined also raises the specter of costs: dollar costs and energy costs. I am not impressed by either. With regard to dollar costs: first, in most manufactured goods the cost of the raw material is only a small fraction of the total cost, the bulk being costs of manufacture, distribution, and marketing. Second, the events of the past few months have made it clear that mineral raw materials from abroad may not be available at the prices of the past. Third, we worry a great deal about a few cents extra in the cost of a pound of metal. But what is the economic cost of transfer of mining and mining-based industries abroad, in terms of employment, contribution to the economy, and breadth of a nation's industry?

As to energy costs, I think the time has come when this nation must recognize, indeed must fully understand, that minerals are the basis of our way of life, and that the use of energy for producing mineral raw materials must have a high priority.

The pursuit of the alternative I have suggested could not be along a single track. The main emphasis would be on shifting technology toward the use of the abundant domestic resources, but this effort would have to be supplemented by efforts toward the discovery of new conventional deposits, toward the recognition of new types of mineral resources, toward more efficient recycling, and toward the elimination of uses that are unnecessary or even frivolous.

The first essential would be a long-term view of the problem of mineral supply. Hasty recourse to immediately available reserves, of lead and zinc for example, might achieve a short-lived self-sufficiency, but it could lead to rapid exhaustion of reserves of critical materials.

I am well aware that complete self-sufficiency for the United States is unattainable, but a much nearer approach to it seems possible if we discard the working principles that have decreased our self-sufficiency in the past. No one can be certain that the price of a new policy would not be a decrease in the versatility of American technology and industry, but certainly there would be a reduced fragility and a reduced vulnerability to the hazards of a divided world. Certainly we have never given the alternative a trial. We have not even wholeheartedly addressed the problem of development of our national mineral resources. We have never had the basis for such an effort. This nation has sent geologists and engineers to every corner of the Free World, but has mapped less than half of its area on scales that would serve as a basis for modern mineral exploration. Regional geophysical surveys of the nation are pitifully inadequate. We are among the backward nations of the world in investigating the geology of our country. Again, it has been easier and cheaper to go abroad for minerals. It may be true that this approach has served our interests in the past, but perhaps it is time to appraise its potential future costs, and to consider whether there are not, indeed, alternatives for our survival.

Index

Alaska Pipe Line Bill, 12

Alternatives to survival: are there alternatives?, 67–68; controlled technology for survival, 80; need for long-term view, 79; need for mineral information, 68; need for resource studies, 80; survival defined, 67; United States, a backward nation in mineral resource studies, 80

American Mining Congress: suggests legislation, 27; views of, on federal oil and gas corporation, 42–43; views of, on mineral leasing laws, 44; views of, on surface mining legislation, 32–38

Bergsten, Fred: views of, on mineral cartels, 48

Brookings Institute: views of Fred Bergsten and Philip Trezise on mineral cartels, 48

Bureau of Mines: working to solve mineral problems, 26

Canada's Department of Energy, Mines and Resources: view of,

on lack of mineral availability, 48

Cartels, 48

CIPEC countries: possible copper embargo by, 62

"Club of Rome": warning by, of mineral shortages, 47–48

Conservation: as essential to mineral supply, 76–78; lip service to, 76

Controlled technology: as an alternative for survival, 75; decrease in dependence on mineral imports produced by, 75; energy cost of, 79; need for, 75; shift of technology to abundant domestic resources produced by, 79; specter of cost for, 78–79

Council on Environmental Quality: continuing analysis by, 41

Department of Energy and Natural Resources: recommendation to create, 13

Economic Stabilization Act of 1971: and importance of free

DESIGNED BY GARY GORE
COMPOSED BY THE COMPOSING ROOM, GRAND RAPIDS, MICHIGAN
MANUFACTURED BY MALLOY LITHOGRAPHING, INC.,
ANN ARBOR, MICHIGAN
TEXT IS SET IN PRESS ROMAN, DISPLAY LINES
IN UNIVERS, AIRPORT TOURIST, AND PRESS ROMAN

ᛋᚼᛉ

Library of Congress Cataloging in Publication Data
Main entry under title:

Politics, minerals, and survival.

Includes index.
1. Mineral industries—United States—Congresses.
I. Marsden, Ralph W., 1911–   ed. II. Society of
Economic Geologists. III. Society of Mining Engineers
of AIME. Mining and Exploration Division.
HD9506.U62P65   338.2'0973   74-27310
ISBN 0-299-06810-2
ISBN 0-299-06814-5 pbk.